Bill Grogan's Goat

Illustrations by
Alan and Lea Daniel

Bill Grogan's goat
(not a chicken but a goa

as feeling fine
ot sick but fine)—

3

Ate three red shirts
(not socks but shirts)

ght off the line
ot a circle but a line).

Bill chased that goat
(not a chicken but a goa

way out back
(not front but back)—

That goat got stuck
(not loose but stuck)

the railroad track

he railroad track).

The whistle blew
(not red but blue).
The train came near
(not far but near).

I Grogan's goat
ot a chicken but a goat),
 shook with fear
ot cheer but fear).

He gave three groans
(not moans but groans)

awful pain
ot joy but pain),

coughed up those shirts (not socks but shirts),

nd flagged the train
nd flagged the train).